THE ULTIMATE
BORUSSIA DORTMUND
TRIVIA BOOK

A Collection of Amazing Trivia Quizzes
and Fun Facts for Die-Hard BVB Fans!

Ray Walker

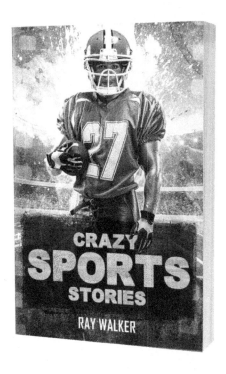

CONTENTS

INTRODUCTION

The intriguing history of Borussia Dortmund can be traced back to a German pub in 1909, when several soccer players formed the club. After years of hard work, the team started to taste success and the silverware started to roll in. This resulted in promotion to the Bundesliga and the opportunity to solidify the club's name among Germany and Europe's top sides.

Known as BVB or the Black and Yellows (Die Schwarzgelben) by many of their passionate fans, the club has consistently been one of the top squads domestically and internationally, although there was a low ebb from 1972 to 1975 when they were relegated and had to compete in Germany's second tier.

Dortmund fans can certainly recognize a good thing when they see it and that's why their home ground is the largest in the nation, with room for more than 83,000 supporters. The team's average attendance is one of the highest on the globe because Dortmund provides plenty of entertaining value game after game.

Like all soccer teams, Dortmund has experienced its fair share of peaks and valleys but they've been competing in the top-flight Bundesliga continuously for close to half a century now.

Dortmund fans greatly appreciate the tremendous effort the club puts forth on the pitch week after week and are confident it will pay off in more silverware just down the road.

Some of the top Dortmund players and managers are given their due in this trivia book including unforgettable names such as Wolfgang Paul, Siegfried Held, Lothar Huber, Manfred Burgsmüller, Michael Zorc, Stefan Reuter, Sebastian Kehl, Mats Hummels, Marco Reus, Matthias Sammer, Robert Lewandowski, Roman Weidenfeller, Hermann Heppenhoff, Ottmar Hitzfield, Udo Lattek, and Jürgen Klopp.

This trivia book was created to celebrate and honor Borussia Dortmund's monumental achievements and history as well as their loyal supporters by looking fondly taking a look back and including events up until January 1, 2021.

The club's ongoing story is told here in entertaining and educational quiz form with 12 unique chapters, each with a different topic. Each section contains 20 inspiring quiz questions along with 10 compelling "Did you know" facts. The questions are presented in 15 multiple-choice and 5 true-or-false options, with the answers on a separate page.

This is the ideal book to challenge and update your knowledge on the enthralling history of Borussia Dortmund and to lay down the gauntlet when challenging other fans to the ultimate Dortmund quiz showdowns. We trust the trivia book will help educate and refresh fans' knowledge of their favorite club and adequately prepare them for every upcoming quiz challenge.

CHAPTER 1:

ORIGINS & HISTORY

QUIZ TIME!

1. What year was Borussia Dortmund founded?

    a. 1907

    b. 1908

    c. 1909

    d. 1910

2. Franz Jacobi and Heinrich Unger were two of the club's key founding members.

    a. True

    b. False

3. What was NOT one of the colors on Dortmund's original kit?

    a. Blue

    b. Green

    c. Red

    d. White

4. Who did Dortmund play its first official match against on January 15, 1911?

   a. SV Werder Bremen
   b. FC Schalke 04
   c. VfB Dortmund
   d. FC Borussia

5. What was Dortmund's first stadium and where the team played its first official match?

   a. Eichwald Stadion
   b. Weiße Wiese Stadion
   c. Stadion Rote Erde
   d. Westfalenstadion

6. What was the score of Dortmund's first official match and victory?

   a. 2-0
   b. 4-0
   c. 6-3
   d. 9-3

7. After World War II, an attempted merger of Dortmund and two other clubs saw the creation of "Sportgemeinschaft Borussia von 1898." which was quickly abandoned.

   a. True
   b. False

8. In 1911-12, Dortmund started competing for the West German Championship in which division of German football?

a. D-Klasse

b. C-Klasse

c. B-Klasse

d. A-Klasse

9. Which club did Dortmund play against in their first Bundesliga contest?

a. Werder Bremen

b. VfR Mannheim

c. Karlsruher FC

d. TSV 1860 Munich

10. What was the final score of Dortmund's first Bundesliga match?

a. 0-2 loss

b. 1-1 draw

c. 2-0 win

d. 2-3 loss

11. As of 2020, how many times has the Dortmund crest been changed?

a. 4

b. 5

c. 6

d. 7

12. In 1913, Dortmund introduced its first black and yellow kits.

a. True

b. False

13. As of 2020, how many times has Dortmund been relegated?

    a. 1

    b. 2

    c. 3

    d. The club has never been relegated.

14. What does Dortmund's slogan, "Echt Liebe," translate to?

    a. One Love

    b. Forever Loyal

    c. True Love

    d. True Passion

15. What league did Dortmund join after the end of the Second World War?

    a. 1. Bezirksklasse

    b. 2. Bezirksklasse

    c. Regionaliga Südwest

    d. Landesliga Westfalen

16. Dortmund was the first team to score a goal in the Bundesliga.

    a. True

    b. False

17. Where did Dortmund get the name "Borussia" from when the club was founded?

    a. The local Borussia Brewery

    b. Borussia Park, where the founders played on Sundays

    c. Borussia roughly translates to "smoke-storm," referring to the town's poor air quality from local factories

d. The Latin word for "Prussia" is Borussia and Dortmund had a large Prussian population

18. In Dortmund's first season in the Bundesliga, in what place did the club finish?

    a. 2nd
    b. 3rd
    c. 4th
    d. 5th

19. What year did Dortmund get relegated from the Bundesliga for the first time?

    a. 1971
    b. 1972
    c. 1973
    d. 1974

20. Dortmund has played its home games at Westfalenstadion since 1978.

    a. True
    b. False

QUIZ ANSWERS

1. C – 1909

2. A – True

3. B – Green

4. C – VfB Dortmund

5. B – Weiße Wiese Stadion

6. D – 9-3

7. A – True

8. B – C-Klasse

9. A – Werder Bremen

10. D – 2-3 loss

11. C – 6

12. A – True

13. A – 1

14. C – True Love

15. D – Landesliga Westfalen

16. A – True

17. A – The local Borussia Brewery

18. C – 4th

19. B – 1972

20. B – False

DID YOU KNOW?

1. Ballspielverein Borussia 09 e.V. Dortmund is the official full name for the Borussia Dortmund soccer club, which plays in the German Bundesliga. The team is typically known simply as BVB or Dortmund, though. Among its nicknames are Die Borussen, Die Schwarzgelben (The Black and Yellows), and Der BVB (The BVB). The club is located in Dortmund, North Rhine-Westphalia in Germany.

2. The club was formed by several soccer players on Dec. 19, 1909, and the soccer team is just one part of a large membership-based sports club. As of January 2021, the Borussia Dortmund club was the second largest in Germany by membership, behind rivals Bayern Munich. The club also includes other popular sports teams such as women's handball.

3. The founders of the team wanted to form a new club because they weren't pleased about playing with the local Trinity Youth organization, which was operated by the Catholic church. The local priest, Father Dewald, was regarded as too stern and he attempted to stop the players from organizing a new club. However, his protests fell on deaf ears as Borussia Dortmund was born soon afterward.

4. The founding members of the club were reportedly Hans Debest, Henry Cleve, Paul Dziendzielle, Hans Kahn,

Gustav Müller, Franz Risse, Fritz Schulte, Hans Siebold, August Tönnesmann, Fritz Weber, and Franz Wendt, along with Heinrich and Robert Unger, Paul and Franz Braun and Franz, Julius, and Wilhelm Jacobi. The name Borussia is Latin for Prussia; however, the club was named after the local Borussia brewery.

5. The team's original kits consisted of blue and white striped shirts with a red sash, along with black shorts. They changed to black and yellow shirts, shorts, and socks in 1913, with the shorts being predominantly back and the socks mainly yellow. The color of the home kit is why one of the club's nicknames is die Schwarzgelben.

6. The team started by playing in local leagues and came close to bankruptcy in 1929. This was because the club signed several professional players and went into debt. However, local fans helped save the day by paying off the club's financial debt.

7. When the Third Reich gained power in the 1930s, the president of the club was replaced after refusing to join the Nazi Party. The team then competed in the newly formed Gauliga Westfalen league and formed a heated rivalry with Schalke 04, which was the most successful team of the day.

8. Allied occupation of Germany following World War II meant that the country's sports organizations were dissolved to distance them from the recent Nazi regime. Borussia Dortmund attempted to merge with two other

clubs, Freier Sportverein 98 and Werksportgemeinschaft Hoesch, with the new organization being called Sportgemeinschaft Borussia von 1898. However, when Dortmund played in the 1949 national final they were known as Ballspielverein Borussia (BVB).

9. The club competed in the Oberliga West from 1946 to 1963. This was one of Germany's top first division leagues, which reached the height of popularity during the late 1950s. Borussia reached the league final in 1949 but was edged 3-2 by VfR Mannheim in extra time. They won the national title for the first time in 1956 by doubling Karlsruher SC 4-2 and successfully defended it a year later with a 4-1 victory over Hamburger SV.

10. Borussia won its third title and the last German football championship in 1963 before the Bundesliga was formed to begin play in 1963-64. The 1963 championship meant Borussia was one of 16 teams admitted to the Bundesliga. Its main league rivals now included neighbors Schalke 04 and Bayern Munich. Games against Schalke are known as the Revierderby while those contested with Bayern Munich are known as Der Klassiker.

CHAPTER 2:

THE CAPTAIN CLASS

QUIZ TIME!

1. Who was the club's first captain in the Bundesliga era?

    a. Friedhelm Konietzka

    b. Alfred Schmidt

    c. Reinhold Wosab

    d. Wilhelm Sturm

2. As of 2021, Dortmund has had 60 captains since its formation.

    a. True

    b. False

3. Who was the longest-serving captain of the team?

    a. Frank Mill

    b. Dirk Hupe

    c. Wolfgang Paul

    d. Michael Zorc

4. Which player was named captain in 1971?

   a. Dieter Kurrat

   b. Werner Lorant

   c. Jürgen Wilhelm

   d. Manfred Ritschel

5. How many seasons did Manfred Burgsmüller skipper Dortmund?

   a. 2

   b. 3

   c. 4

   d. 5

6. Dortmund named which player captain in 1998, a position he held until 2003?

   a. Harry Decheiver

   b. Andreas Möller

   c. Stefan Reuter

   d. Jürgen Kohler

7. Mats Hummels captained Dortmund for half the season in 2009-10.

   a. True

   b. False

8. How many captains has Dortmund had in the Bundesliga?

   a. 13

   b. 15

   c. 18

   d. 20

9. Who was captain from 1983 to 1985?

   a. Herbert Hein
   b. Michael Zorc
   c. Bernd Klotz
   d. Rolf Rüssmann

10. Which player was named captain in 1974?

    a. Klaus Ackermann
    b. Mirko Votava
    c. Lothar Huber
    d. Hans-Werner Hartl

11. How many different players captained Dortmund between 2000 and 2020?

    a. 7
    b. 6
    c. 5
    d. 4

12. Reinhold Richter was the club's first captain in 1911.

    a. True
    b. False

13. Who did Dortmund name captain in 2003?

    a. Torsten Frings
    b. Stefan Reuter
    c. Christoph Metzelder
    d. Lars Ricken

14. How many seasons did Mats Hummels serve as captain?

    a. 3

    b. 4

    c. 1

    d. 2

15. Who did Dortmund name as captain ahead of the 2018-19 campaign?

    a. Mahmoud Dahoud

    b. Maximilian Philipp

    c. Marco Reus

    d. Mario Götze

16. Between 1963 and 1971, Dortmund had five different captains.

    a. True

    b. False

17. Which player was named the vice-captain for the 2019-20 season?

    a. Łukasz Piszczek

    b. Thorgan Hazard

    c. Mats Hummels

    d. Nico Schulz

18. How many years did Michael Zorc serve as Dortmund's captain?

    a. 7

    b. 8

    c. 9

    d. 10

19. Who was captain from 2008 to 2014?

    a. Uwe Hünemeier
    b. Florian Kringe
    c. Marc Ziegler
    d. Sebastian Kehl

20. Jan Koller was Dortmund's first captain born outside of Germany.

    a. True
    b. False

QUIZ ANSWERS

1. B – Alfred Schmidt

2. B – False

3. D – Michael Zorc

4. A – Dieter Kurrat

5. C – 4

6. C – Stefan Reuter

7. B – False

8. C – 18

9. D – Rolf Rüssmann

10. A – Klaus Ackermann

11. A – 7

12. B – False

13. C – Christoph Metzelder

14. D – 2

15. C – Marco Reus

16. B – False

17. A – Łukasz Piszczek

18. C – 9

19. D – Sebastian Kehl

20. B – False

DID YOU KNOW?

1. Since joining the Bundesliga in 1963-64, the club has had 18 full-time captains as of January 2021. They are 1963-65, Alfred Schmidt; 1965-1968, Wolfgang Paul; 1968-1971, Sigfried Held; 1971-1974, Dieter Kurrat; 1974-1977, Klaus Ackermann; 1977-1979, Lothar Huber; 1979-1983, Manfred Burgsmüller; 1983-1985, Rolf Rüssmann; 1985-1987, Dirk Hupe; 1987-1988, Frank Mill; 1988-1998, Michael Zorc; 1998-2003, Stefan Reuter; 2003-2004, Christoph Metzelder; 2004-2008, Christian Wörns; 2008-2014, Sebastian Kehl; 2014-2016, Mats Hummels; 2016-2018, Marcel Schmelzer; and the current captain since 2018 is Marco Reus.

2. The first club skipper after joining the Bundesliga was Alfred Schmidt, who held the position between 1963 and 1965. Nicknamed "Aki," Schmidt was an attacking midfielder who played with Dortmund from 1956 to 1968. He helped the squad capture the German Cup in 1965, the European Cup Winners' Cup the next year, and two league titles before entering the Bundesliga. Schmidt reportedly notched 67 goals in 275 appearances with the club and also represented the German national side 25 times. He entered management after playing and then served as Dortmund's fan correspondent.

3. The longest-serving captain in Dortmund's history was Michael Zorc, who wore the armband from 1988 to 1997.

Zorc also holds the team record for most pieces of silverware while acting as skipper as he helped them hoist a pair of Bundesliga titles, a German Cup, three German Supercups, an Intercontinental Cup, and the European Champions League. Zorc was a central midfielder nicknamed "Susi" and he played with Dortmund for his entire pro career between 1981 and 1998.

4. German international center-back Mats Hummels was a popular captain with Dortmund from 2014 to 2016. He spent his youth career and the start of his pro career with Bayern Munich before joining Dortmund on loan in 2008-09. The club bought him in 2009 and he stayed until 2016, when he went back to Bayern. However, Hummels returned to Dortmund in June 2019, when the 30-year-old was reacquired. As of 2020, he had won two straight Bundesliga titles with Dortmund in 2010-11 and 2011-12, along with a German Cup and three German Supercups.

5. Former German international defender/midfielder Stefan Reuter was the acting captain between 1998 and 2003 and he played for the club from 1992 to 2004. He played for 1. FC Nürnberg and Bayern Munich to kick off his pro career before a spell with Juventus in Italy. Reuter helped Dortmund capture the Bundesliga in 1994–95, 1995–96, and 2001–02, along with two German Supercups, an Intercontinental Cup, and the European Champions League. In addition, the side reached the final of the 1993 and 2002 UEFA Cup. Nicknamed "Turbo" due to his

speed, Reuter played over 300 Bundesliga games with the team.

6. Christian Wörns began his career with Waldhof Mannheim as a 17-year-old in 1989 before moving on to Bayer Leverkusen two years later. He then tried his luck with French side Paris Saint-Germain in 1998-99 before moving to Dortmund for the last decade of his career. The German international defender captained the squad between 2004 and 2008 before retiring and entering the world of management. Wörns played over 300 league matches with the outfit and helped them win the Bundesliga in 2001-02.

7. Another long-serving Dortmund skipper was German international midfielder Sebastian Walter Kehl, who played with the club from 2002 to 2015 and wore the armband between 2008 and 2014. Dortmund acquired him from SC Freiburg in January 2002 and he went on to appear in more than 360 games with the team, helping to win three league crowns, a German Cup, and two German Supercups. Kehl also took home a runners-up medal from the 2012-13 European Champions League.

8. Left-back Marcel Schmelzer has been with Dortmund since making his pro debut with the side in 2008. He played every minute of the 2010-11 campaign, when the club won the league championship. The German international was named captain in August 2016, when he took over from Mats Hummel, and he wore the armband until giving it up to Marco Reus two years later. As of 2020, Schmelzer had

helped his side win two straight league titles, two German Cups, three German Supercups, and a runners-up medal in the 2012-13 European Champions League.

9. Frank Mill was one of Dortmund's shortest-serving skippers as he held the position from 1987 to 1988. The German international striker and former Olympic team player joined the side from Borussia Mönchengladbach in 1986 and stayed until 1994, when he joined Fortuna Düsseldorf. Mill helped the team win the German Cup in 1988-89 and took home a runners-up medal from the 1992-93 European Champions League. He also scored nearly 50 goals in just under 200 league matches with the side.

10. Another player to hold the club captaincy for just over a year was German international center-back Christoph Metzelder, who was handed the armband from 2003-04. He joined the side in 2000 from Preußen Münster and remained until 2007, when he headed to Real Madrid. Metzelder missed the entire 2003-04 season due to an Achilles tendon injury that sidelined him for approximately 18 months and he played just under 160 games with the club before leaving. However, he did help the side win the league title in 2001-02.

CHAPTER 3:

AMAZING MANAGERS

QUIZ TIME!

1. Who acted as the club's manager in 1923?

   a. Willi Sevcik

   b. Ernst Kuzorra

   c. Paul Dziendzielle

   d. Tony Cargnelli

2. Dortmund has had 15 managers in the Bundesliga era.

   a. True

   b. False

3. Which club did Omar Hitzfeld manage before joining Dortmund in 1991?

   a. Grasshoppers Club Zürich

   b. Bayern Munich

   c. SC Zug

   d. FC Aarau

4. How many seasons did Jürgen Klopp manage Dortmund in the Bundesliga?

a. 5

b. 6

c. 7

d. 8

5. Which former player was signed as manager on July 1, 1985?

   a. Uli Maslo

   b. Friedhelm Konietzka

   c. Pál Csernai

   d. Reinhard Saftig

6. Which club did Carl-Heinz Rühl manage before coming to Dortmund?

   a. VfL Osnabrück

   b. Karlsruher SC

   c. TSV 1860 Munich

   d. MSV Duisburg

7. Dortmund fired manager Lucien Favre after a 5-1 loss to VfB Stuttgart on December 12, 2020.

   a. True

   b. False

8. Who did Dortmund name as manager in 2004?

   a. Jürgen Röber

   b. Bert van Marwijk

   c. Michael Skibbe

   d. Matthias Sammer

9. Who did Dortmund sign as manager on July 1, 1988?

    a. Erich Ribbeck

    b. Nevio Scala

    c. Horst Köppel

    d. Reinhard Saftig

10. Who did Jürgen Klopp replace as manager in 2008?

    a. Thomas Tuchel

    b. Jürgen Röber

    c. Thomas Doll

    d. Peter Bosz

11. How many different managers did Dortmund have between 2000 and 2010?

    a. 5

    b. 6

    c. 7

    d. 8

12. Dortmund has had a total of 75 managers in its history.

    a. True

    b. False

13. Which club did Dortmund hire Peter Bosz from in 2017?

    a. Ajax

    b. SBV Vitesse

    c. Heracles Almelo

    d. Maccabi Tel Aviv FC

14. Who was Dortmund's first manager in the Bundesliga era?

    a. Heinz Murach

    b. Max Merkel

    c. Willi Multhaup

    d. Hermann Eppenhoff

15. Which club did Lucien Favre manage before joining Dortmund in 2018?

    a. Servette FC

    b. FC Zürich

    c. OGC Nice

    d. Borussia Mönchengladbach

16. Branko Zebec was Dortmund's first manager born outside of Germany.

    a. True

    b. False

17. What year was Udo Lattek first appointed as Dortmund's manager?

    a. 1978

    b. 1979

    c. 1980

    d. 1981

18. Who was named manager on Dec. 13, 2020, after the departure of Lucien Favre?

    a. Edin Terzić

    b. Manfred Stefes

    c. Peter Stöger

    d. Eduard Havlicek

19. How many trophies did Ottmar Hitzfeld win with Dortmund?

    a. 3
    b. 4
    c. 5
    d. 6

20. As 0f 2020, Dortmund has had 10 temporary caretakers.

    a. True
    b. False

QUIZ ANSWERS

1. D – Tony Cargnelli

2. B – False

3. A – Grasshoppers Club Zürich

4. C – 7

5. C – Pál Csernai

6. D – MSV Duisburg

7. A – True

8. B – Bert van Marwijk

9. C – Jorst Köppel

10. C – Thomas Doll

11. D – 8

12. B – False

13. A – Ajax

14. D – Herman Eppenhoff

15. C – OGC Nice

16. B – False

17. B – 1979

18. A – Edin Terzić

19. C – 5

20. B – False

DID YOU KNOW?

1. Borussia Dortmund has employed approximately 60 club managers since 1923, with Tony Cargnelli believed to be the first between January 1923 and December 21, 1923. The next known official managers are Fritz Thelen and Ernst Kuzorra, who are believed to have shared the job from July 1935 to July 1936. There are no official managers listed between June 1939 and January 1946 due to World War II.

2. Tony Cargnelli, who's believed to be the club's first acting manager in 1923, was an Austria-born former player who managed numerous famous teams, most of them in Italy, between 1927 and 1950. Clubs he later managed in Italy include Torino, Palermo, Bari, Inter Milan, Bologna, and Lazio.

3. Since Dortmund joined the Bundesliga in 1963, there have been a reported 38 different managers with the club. The list begins with Hermann Eppenhoff between 1963 and 1965 and ends with current manager Edin Terzić, who took over the squad on December 13, 2020, as interim boss until the end of the 2020-21 campaign. Terzić was previously an assistant manager with the club starting in 2018.

4. Udo Lattek had two stints as manager, from July 1, 1979, to May 10, 1981, and from April 14, 2000, to June 30, 2000. His second stint consisted of just five league games, which included two wins, two draws, and a defeat. That enabled

Dortmund to end the season just above the relegation zone and remain in the Bundesliga. Lattek failed to win any silverware with the club but won plenty while managing Bayern Munich, Borussia Mönchengladbach, and Barcelona.

5. The shortest managerial stint in Dortmund history was the two days that Reinhard Saftig was in charge. He took over on October 25, 1984, from Tino Koietzka and was replaced just over 48 hours and one game later by Erich Ribbeck. However, Saftig returned as manager on April 20, 1986, and remained until June 26, 1988. He went on to manage several other German clubs and also spent some time in Turkey. He then returned to Dortmund in 2003 for a couple of years as a scout.

6. The longest-serving manager in Dortmund's history so far was Jürgen Klopp, who was in charge of the team from July 1, 2008, to June 30, 2015, for a total of 2,555 days and 318 games. Klopp posted a record of 180 wins, 65 draws, and 73 losses for an average of 1.90 points per game. He previously managed Mainz 05 between 2001 and 2008 and he left Dortmund in 2015 to carry on with Liverpool of the English Premier League. Klopp helped guide Dortmund to two straight league titles in 2010-11 and 2011-12, along with a German Cup in 2011-12 for a League and Cup double, and two straight German Supercups in 2013 and 2014.

7. Ottmar Hitzfield came to Dortmund from Grasshoppers in Zürich, Switzerland, and held the job from July 1, 1991, to June 30, 1997, to rank as the club's second longest-serving

boss. Hitzfield was on the job for 2,191 days and 273 games. He helped the club capture two consecutive league crowns in 1994-95 and 1995-96, as well as the German Supercup in 1995 and 1996. His biggest achievement was the European Champions League title in 1996-97. He later managed Bayern Munich to a Champions League title. He was manager of the Swiss national team from 2008 to 2014.

8. In 1966, Dortmund became the first German side to win a European trophy when they took the European Cup Winners' Cup with Willi Multhaup as manager. He was with the team from July 1, 1965, for just one year after coming over from Werder Bremen, where he had won the 1964-65 Bundesliga. Multhaup headed to 1. FC Köln after departing Dortmund and won the German Cup with them in 1967-68.

9. Former German international defender/midfielder Matthias Sammer made a name for himself as a player with Dynamo Dresden, VfB Stuttgart, and Inter Milan before starring for Dortmund from 1993 to 1998. He was just 33 years old when he took over as manager of the club on July 1, 2000. He led the side to the Bundesliga title in 2001-2002, as well as reaching the UEFA Cup final where they were beaten 3-2 by Dutch club Feyenoord. After the club finished in sixth place in the Bundesliga in 2003-04, Sammer was sacked and he took over as manager of VfB Stuttgart.

10. Although he had a winning percentage of 61.82, Lucien Favre was in charge of the club for just over two years

from May 2018 to December 13, 2020, when he was fired. Favre posted 68 wins, 18 draws, and 24 defeats and led the team to the 2019 German Supercup. He also went unbeaten in the first 15 matches of the 2018-19 Bundesliga season to set a club record. However, the former Swiss international midfielder was let go after several poor results, including a 5-1 home loss to newly-promoted VfB Stuttgart.

CHAPTER 4:

GOALTENDING GREATS

QUIZ TIME!

1. How many clean sheets did Roman Weidenfeller record in the 2011-12 Bundesliga?

    a. 9

    b. 10

    c. 13

    d. 15

2. Goalkeeper Stefan Klos played over 400 games for Dortmund in all competitions.

    a. True

    b. False

3. Which keeper made 32 starts in 1990-91?

    a. Wolfgang de Beer

    b. Stefan Klos

    c. Rolf Meyer

    d. Dirk Galeski

4. Which keeper played 15 games in 2007-08?

    a. Marc Ziegler

    b. Alexander Bade

    c. Marcel Höttecke

    d. Roman Weidenfeller

5. How many wins did Roman Bürki have in the 2018-19 Bundesliga?

    a. 16

    b. 18

    c. 20

    d. 21

6. Which keeper played four games as Dortmund's second option in the 2019-20 Bundesliga league?

    a. Luca Unbehaun

    b. Eric Oelschlägel

    c. Marwin Hitz

    d. Jonas Hupe

7. Roman Weidenfeller was the first Dortmund keeper to win the IFFHS World's Best Goalkeeper award.

    a. True

    b. False

8. Who backed up Roman Weidenfeller in the 2013-14 season?

    a. Mitchell Langerak

    b. Dominik Reimann

    c. Roman Bürki

    d. Marc Ziegler

9. How many clean sheets did Roman Bürki post in 2019-20 Bundesliga matches?

    a. 10
    b. 11
    c. 12
    d. 13

10. Which keeper had five draws in 2005-06 league matches?

    a. Dennis Gentenaar
    b. Guillaume Warmuz
    c. Alexander Bade
    d. Dominik Reimann

11. How many Bundesliga games did Roman Weidenfeller win in 2010-11?

    a. 22
    b. 20
    c. 10
    d. 14

12. Wolfgang de Beer played over 300 matches for Dortmund.

    a. True
    b. False

13. How many wins did Stefan Klos record in the 1994-95 Bundesliga season?

    a. 17
    b. 18
    c. 19
    d. 20

14. Which keeper drew Bundesliga contests in 1999-00?

    a. Wolfgang de Beer
    b. Marcel Höttecke
    c. Jens Lehmann
    d. Philipp Laux

15. How many league wins did Guillaume Warmuz have in the 2003-04 campaign?

    a. 10
    b. 9
    c. 8
    d. 7

16. Jens Lehmann scored a goal in open play against FC Schalke 04 in 1998-99.

    a. True
    b. False

17. How many goals did keeper Roman Bürki allow in 2017-18 domestic league matches?

    a. 34
    b. 38
    c. 43
    d. 50

18. Which keeper played five games in 2001-02 as Dortmund's backup?

    a. Harald Schumacher
    b. Wolfgang de Beer
    c. Luca Unbehaun
    d. Philipp Laux

19. How many Bundesliga wins did Stefan Klos register in 1997-98?

    a. 7
    b. 10
    c. 11
    d. 14

20. Keeper Jens Lehmann was once suspended for kicking opponent Soumaila Coulibaly in the 18-yard box.

    a. True
    b. False

QUIZ ANSWERS

1. D – 15

2. B – False

3. A – Wolfgang de Beer

4. A – Marc Ziegler

5. D – 21

6. C – Marwin Hitz

7. B – False

8. A – Mitchell Langerak

9. D – 13

10. A – Dennis Gentenaar

11. A – 22

12. B – False

13. D – 20

14. C – Jens Lehmann

15. B – 9

16. B – False

17. C – 43

18. D – Philipp Laux

19. C – 11

20. A – True

DID YOU KNOW?

1. Dortmund's number one goalkeeper in their first season in the Bundesliga was Hans Tilkowski, who joined the club in 1963 and played until 1967, when he joined Eintracht Frankfurt. He helped the squad win the German Cup in 1964-65 and the European Cup Winners' Cup the next season, when Dortmund finished as runners-up in the Bundesliga. He was also named the German Footballer of the Year for 1965. Tilkowski's most famous game was probably the 1966 World Cup Final when West Germany was beaten 4-2 in extra time by hosts England.

2. Roman Weidenfeller was acquired by Dortmund in 2002 on a free transfer from 1. FC Kaiserslautern and remained with the club until he ended his playing days in 2018. He helped the side win the 2010-11 Bundesliga and the League and German Cup Double the next season. However, he was injured in the German Cup final after colliding with Mario Gómez at the 33rd minute and substituted. The German international then guided the team to the 2013 German Supercup over rivals Bayern Munich and won another German Cup in 2017. Weidenfeller retired after more than 450 games with the club and stayed with Dortmund as an international ambassador.

3. Another goalie named Roman joined the club in June 2015, when Roman Bürki arrived from SC Freiburg. He had

played over 220 games with the team as of January 2021 and helped it hoist the German Cup in 2016-17. The Swiss international became the first Bundesliga keeper to post five clean sheets in his first five games of the season to kick off the 2017-18 campaign. Bürki's younger brother Marco Bürki is currently a defender with FC Luzern in Switzerland.

4. Stefan Klos was a hometown boy who played over 350 times with Dortmund between 1990 and 1998, when he moved to Glasgow Rangers in Scotland. He helped Dortmund win back-to-back league titles in 1994-1995 and 1995-1996 and played every contest in the 1996-97 Bundesliga, as well as 11 Champions League matches to help the club win that trophy for the first time. Klos also won two German Supercups and an Intercontinental Cup with the team.

5. Horst Bertram spent a dozen years with Dortmund after arriving in 1971 and appeared in over 200 games with the club, with just under half of them coming in the Bundesliga. He also kept 65 clean sheets in those games before retiring and becoming a coach. Bertram played with Dortmund during the lean years and wasn't able to help the team capture any silverware. They were relegated in 1972 but Bertram helped them earn promotion back to the Bundesliga in 1975-76.

6. Eike Immel was just 17 years old when he joined Horst Bertram in goal in the 1978-79 season and he stayed with

the club until 1986, when he joined VfB Stuttgart. The German international set a new Bundesliga transfer fee for a goalkeeper at the time when he was sold for 2 million Deutsche Marks. Immel made 534 appearances in the Bundesliga and conceded a league-record 829 goals. He played 279 times with Dortmund with 61 clean sheets but wasn't able to help the side win any silverware.

7. Although he retired from his position as a goalkeeping coach with the club in 2018 to become the fan relations manager, Wolfing de Beer, who was nicknamed "Teddy," also played with the club from 1986 to 2001 after joining from MSV Duisburg. He helped the side win a German Cup, a German Supercup, an Intercontinental Cup, and the 1996-97 European Champions League. He played over 200 matches with the club and posted 62 clean sheets.

8. One of the best-known Dortmund goalkeepers was German international Jens Lehmann, who came over from AC Milan in Italy in 1999 after starting his pro career with Schalke 04 from 1988 to 1998. Lehmann, who took over in goal from Stefan Klos, stayed with Dortmund until 2003, when he joined Arsenal of the English Premier League. He helped Dortmund take the 2001-02 Bundesliga and reach the final of the UEFA Cup the same season. As of 2020, Lehmann shares the record for most red cards for a Dortmund player and the most for a Bundesliga goalie with three of them.

9. Veteran goalkeeper Marwin Hitz joined the team in 2018-19 to back up number one Roman Bürki after Roman Weidenfeller left. He was still with them in January 2021. The Swiss international came over from FC Augsburg after previously playing in Germany with VfL Wolfsburg and starting his career in his homeland. He was on the squad that won the 2019 German Supercup while winning the Bundesliga a decade earlier with Wolfsburg. Hitz is famous for scoring an injury-time equalizer against Bayer 04 Leverkusen in 2015.

10. Philipp Laux began his pro career with Borussia Dortmund in 1993-94 and played with the reserve team. He then moved to regional club SSV Ulm and helped them earn promotion to the 2. Bundesliga in 1998 and promotion to the Bundesliga a year later. However, they were relegated the next season. Laux's fine play earned him another shot with Dortmund though, and he spent 2000 to 2002 at the Westfalenstadion as a backup, helping the team win the 2001-02 Bundesliga and reach the UEFA Cup final.

CHAPTER 5:

DARING DEFENDERS

QUIZ TIME!

1. Which defender played 33 domestic league matches in 1988-89?

   a. Bernd Storck

   b. Günter Kutowski

   c. Robert Nikolic

   d. Matthias Ruländer

2. Lothar Huber played over 390 Bundesliga matches with Dortmund.

   a. True

   b. False

3. Which defender recorded 6 assists in 2018-19 league games?

   a. Łukasz Piszczek

   b. Achraf Hakimi

   c. Marcel Schmelzer

   d. Abdou Diallo

4. How many Bundesliga goals did Mats Hummels score in 2010-11?

   a. 2
   b. 3
   c. 4
   d. 5

5. Which defender posted 2 goals and 2 assists in the 1999-2000 Bundesliga?

   a. Dedé
   b. Christian Wörns
   c. Jürgen Kohler
   d. Karsten Baumann

6. Which left-back scored 8 goals in 2019-20 domestic league matches?

   a. Raphaël Guerreiro
   b. Manuel Akimji
   c. Nico Schulz
   d. Marco Rente

7. Dedé made 122 Bundesliga appearances with Dortmund.

   a. True
   b. False

8. Which defender scored 3 goals in the 2012-13 Bundesliga season?

   a. Marian Sarr
   b. Marcel Schmelzer
   c. Felipe Santana
   d. Neven Subotić

9. How many assists did Łukasz Piszczek record in all competitions in 2014-15?

    a. 4
    b. 6
    c. 7
    d. 11

10. Which defender completed 1,643 passes in the 2017-18 Bundesliga?

    a. Marc Bartra
    b. Sokratis Papastathopoulos
    c. Neven Subotić
    d. Ömer Toprak

11. Which defender had 7 assists in all competitions in 2018-19?

    a. Dan-Axel Zagadou
    b. Manuel Akinji
    c. Abdou Diallo
    d. Achraf Hakimi

12. Sokratis Papastathopoulos was shown three red cards in 2013-14 league matches.

    a. True
    b. False

13. Who scored 3 goals in the 2000-01 Bundesliga season?

    a. Dedé
    b. Christian Wörns
    c. Alfred Nijhuis
    d. Christoph Metzelder

14. How many cards was Jörg Heinrich shown in all competitions in 1996-97?

    a. 11
    b. 12
    c. 13
    d. 14

15. Which defender scored 4 goals in all competitions in 2017-18?

    a. Jeremy Toljan
    b. Dan-Axel Zagadou
    c. Jan-Niklas Beste
    d. Marc Bartra

16. Mats Hummels won three league titles with Dortmund.

    a. True
    b. False

17. How many Bundesliga assists did Dedé have in 2007-08?

    a. 10
    b. 9
    c. 8
    d. 7

18. In 2015-16, Matthias Ginter scored how many goals in domestic league games?

    a. 1
    b. 2
    c. 3
    d. 4

19. Which defender had five yellow cards in the 2009-10 Bundesliga?

    a. Manuel Friedrich

    b. Koray Günter

    c. Uwe Hünemeier

    d. Marcel Schmelzer

20. Neven Subotić was shown 11 yellow cards in the 2014-15 Bundesliga season.

    a. True

    b. False

QUIZ ANSWERS

1. B – Günter Kutowski

2. B – False

3. A – Łukasz Piszczek

4. D – 5

5. C – Jürgen Kohler

6. A – Raphaël Guerreiro

7. B – False

8. D – Neven Subotić

9. C – 7

10. D – Ömer Toprak

11. D – Achraf Hakimi

12. B – False

13. B – Christian Wörns

14. C – 12

15. D – Marc Bartra

16. B – False

17. B – 9

18. C – 3

19. D – Marcel Shmelzer

20. B – False

DID YOU KNOW?

1. Brazilian Leonardo de Deus Santos, better known as Dede, played in the back four and midfield during his career with Dortmund, which began in 1998, when he was just 20 years old. Dede remained with the club until 2011, when he left to play in Turkey. He appeared in nearly 400 games with the squad while chipping in with more than a dozen goals and over 50 assists. Dede helped Dortmund win a pair of league titles along with a runners-up medal in the German Cup, German Supercup, and UEFA Cup.

2. Former Dortmund assistant manager Lothar Huber played with the team from 1974 to 1987 after joining from his hometown club 1. FC Kaiserslautern and was acting captain between 1977 and 1979. Huber didn't manage to win any trophies with the club as a player or assistant manager, but he chipped in with his fair share of goals by netting 50 of them in just over 350 appearances. After leaving Dortmund, he went on to manage TSG Sprockhövel.

3. Polish international right-back/center-back Łukasz Piszczek started his career as a prolific striker and joined Dortmund from Hertha BSC on a free transfer in May 2010. He was still with the side as of January 2021. With Dortmund, Piszczek had appeared in close to 400 games as of 2021, with 18 goals to his name. He helped the club win two straight league titles in 2010-11 and 2011-12, as well as

a pair of German Cups and German Supercups. He also picked up a runners-up medal in the 2013 European Champions League and was named to the Bundesliga Team of the Season for 2015-16 and 2016-17.

4. Günter Kutowski was just 19 years old when he joined Dortmund in 1984 after spending his youth with local amateur team 1. FC Paderborn. He remained with the club until 1996 when he left for Rot Weiss Essen and retired at the age of 36 to become a player agent. Kutowski made 344 appearances with the club and chipped in with 5 goals while helping them capture two consecutive league titles in 1994-95 and 1995-96 as well as the 1988-89 German Cup. He also earned a runners-up medal at the UEFA Cup in 1992-93.

5. Neven Subotić was born in the former nation of Yugoslavia and played nationally for Serbia. After moving to the United States, he began playing with the University of South Florida as well as the nation's Under-17 and Under-20 teams. He joined German club 1. FSV Mainz 05 to kick off his pro career in 2007 and joined Dortmund a year later. Subotić's fine performances helped the side win the league in 2010-11 and 2011-12 as well as the German Cup in 2011-12 and the German Supercup in 2013 and 2014. He left in January 2018 to join Saint-Étienne in France after making over 260 appearances with Dortmund.

6. Dortmund native Wilhelm Burgsmüller played most of his career with the club before the Bundesliga era as he was

one of its top defenders between 1952 and 1966. The record books say the gifted center-back played 262 times for the squad but it's unclear if he scored any goals. He helped the side win the German football championship in 1956, 1957, and 1963, which earned Dortmund promotion to the Bundesliga in its inaugural season in 1963-64.

7. German international center-back Jürgen Kohler played over 100 times for Germany and finished his pro career with Dortmund from 1995 to 2002. He joined from Italian giants Juventus, after previously playing with Waldhof Mannheim, 1. FC Köln and Bayern Munich. Kohler helped Dortmund capture the Bundesliga and German Supercup twice, as well as the European Champions League and Intercontinental Cup in 1997. He was also named German Footballer of the Year that season due to his perception, strength, and anticipation. Kohler notched 18 goals in 250 games with the club and entered football management after hanging up his boots.

8. Gerhard Cyliax was another defender who played most of his Dortmund games before the team reached the Bundesliga, as he was with the club from 1959 to 1968. The hometown player began his career with Westfalia Herne in 1955, and then played with SC Preußen Münster until joining Dortmund. He played 243 times for Dortmund, scoring 35 goals, and helped the side hoist the German football championship in 1963, the German Cup in 1964-65, and the European Cup Winners' Cup in 1965-66.

9. Former captain Wolfgang Paul, who wore the armband from 1965 to 1968, played his entire pro career with Dortmund from 1961 to 1971, when he had to retire at the age of 31 due to injury. Paul appeared in 237 matches with the club, with 148 of them coming in the Bundesliga after he helped the side earn promotion in 1963. He also helped them win the German Cup in 1964-65 and the European Cup Winners' Cup the next season. Paul's side reached the German Cup final in 1962-63 and finished as Bundesliga runners-up in 1965-66.

10. German international Kevin Großkreutz of Dortmund played right-back and on the wing, and starred for his hometown club from 2009 to 2015. He joined from Rot Weiss Ahlen and wound up with VfB Stuttgart after leaving. He played 236 contests with the black and yellow and netted 26 goals. Großkreutz also helped the team win the league in 2010-11 and 2011-12 as well as the German Cup in 2011-12 and the German Supercup in 2013 and 2014. He also earned a European Champions League runners-up medal in 2012-13.

CHAPTER 6:

MAESTROS OF THE MIDFIELD

QUIZ TIME!

1. Which midfielder scored 5 goals in the 2008-09 Bundesliga?

    a. Tamás Hajnal

    b. Nuri Şahin

    c. Tinga

    d. Mario Götze

2. Michael Zorc holds the record for the most appearances for Dortmund in all competitions.

    a. True

    b. False

3. Which player had 8 assists in 2010-11 in domestic league matches?

    a. Moritz Leitner

    b. Markus Feulner

    c. Antônio da Silva

    d. Nuri Şahin

4. In 2019-20, Axel Witsel scored how many goals in Bundesliga games?

   a. 4
   b. 5
   c. 6
   d. 7

5. How many all-time career appearances did Michael Zorc make for Dortmund?

   a. 523
   b. 555
   c. 572
   d. 586

6. Which player received 9 yellow cards in the 1999-00 Bundesliga season?

   a. Christian Nerlinger
   b. Miroslav Stević
   c. Francis Bugri
   d. Andreas Möller

7. Knut Reinhart was the only Dortmund midfielder to be shown a red card in the 1995-96 Bundesliga.

   a. True
   b. False

8. How many goals did Matthias Sammer score with Dortmund in the Bundesliga?

   a. 16
   b. 19

c. 21

d. 23

9. Which midfielder scored 4 goals in domestic league games in 1990-91?

a. Günter Breitzke

b. Murdo MacLeod

c. Gerhard Poschner

d. Thomas Franck

10. How many assists did Vladimir But have in 1999-2000 domestic league games?

a. 3

b. 4

c. 5

d. 6

11. Who scored 15 goals for Dortmund in the 1994-95 Bundesliga campaign?

a. Thomas Franck

b. Steffen Freund

c. Andreas Möller

d. Michael Zorc

12. Tamás Hajnal recorded 14 assists in 2008-09 domestic league games.

a. True

b. False

13. How many times did Matthias Sammer win the German Footballer of the Year award with Dortmund?

a. 4

b. 3

c. 2

d. 1

14. Who scored 4 goals in 2013-14 Bundesliga games?

    a. Nuri Şahin

    b. Sven Bender

    c. Erik Durm

    d. Miloš Jojić

15. Tinga led Dortmund in assists in the 2006-07 Bundesliga season with how many?

    a. 4

    b. 5

    c. 6

    d. 7

16. Stefan Reuter played 350 Bundesliga matches with Dortmund.

    a. True

    b. False

17. Which player tallied 7 assists in domestic league matches in the 2015-16 season?

    a. İlkay Gündoğan

    b. Nuri Şahin

    c. Kevin Kampl

    d. Gonzalo Castro

18. Who scored 13 goals in 2011-12 domestic league matches?

    a. Antônio da Silva
    b. Shinji Kagawa
    c. İlkay Gündoğan
    d. Moritz Leitner

19. Which midfielder scored 4 goals and 3 assists in 2004-05 domestic league games?

    a. Sebastian Kehl
    b. Marc-André Kruska
    c. Guy Demel
    d. Salvatore Gambino

20. In 2019-20, Axel Witsel completed 1,700 passes in Bundesliga games.

    a. True
    b. False

QUIZ ANSWERS

1. A – Tamás Hajnal

2. A – True

3. D – Nuri Şahin

4. A – 4

5. C – 572

6. B – Miroslav Stević

7. A – True

8. C – 21

9. C – Gerhard Poschner

10. A – 3

11. D – Michael Zorc

12. B – False

13. C – 2

14. D – Miloš Jojić

15. C – 6

16. B – False

17. D – Gonzalo Castro

18. B – Shinji Kagawa

19. A – Sebastian Kehl

20. B – False

DID YOU KNOW?

1. Nicknamed "Hoppy," midfielder/defender Dieter Kurrat was a dependable fixture in the Dortmund side from 1960 to 1974, helping the team earn promotion to the Bundesliga in 1963 but also seeing them relegated a decade later. Born in Dortmund, Kurrat also helped the team win the German Cup in 1964-65, as well as the European Cup Winner's Cup the next season. He tallied 19 goals in 357 contests and the former captain (1971-1974) also had a short spell as club manager between February and June 1974.

2. Reinhold Wosab played just about anywhere on the pitch during his career because he was just as effective as a defender, midfielder, or striker but was generally known as a right-back. He played with the club from 1962 to 1971, which meant he helped earn promotion to the Bundesliga, and he left to join VfL Bochum just before they were relegated. Wosab was also with the side when it won the UEFA Cup Winners' Cup in 1965-66 and the German Cup the previous season. Wosab is credited with scoring 90 times in 270 outings with the team.

3. Wearing the captain's armband from 1968 to 1971, Sigfried Held was an attacking midfielder/forward who played for the club between 1965 and 1971. He joined from Kickers Offenbach and returned there when leaving Dortmund.

He returned to Dortmund to play between 1977 and 1979, after they had earned promotion back to the Bundesliga in 1976. The German international became a manager after hanging up his boots and was in charge of teams such as Iceland, Malta, and Thailand, before returning to Dortmund to work in fan relations. Held played 259 times with the side while scoring 53 goals and helping them win the European Cup Winners' Cup in 1965-66.

4. German international Lars Ricken spent his entire pro playing career with Dortmund between 1993 and 2007 and, as of January 2021, was with the team as a youth coordinator. As a player, the attacking midfielder helped his hometown club win the Bundesliga in 1994–95, 1995–96, and 2001–02, as well as the German Supercup in 1995 and 1996, and the European Champions League and Intercontinental Cup in 1997. Ricken played 407 times with the first team and registered 69 goals and 68 assists.

5. Before managing Dortmund between 2000 and 2004, Matthias Sammer was one of the world's best midfield players and could also play as a sweeper. Sammer played out his pro career with the club from 1993 to 1998 and also represented East Germany and Germany internationally. He joined in January 1993 from Inter Milan and helped Dortmund capture the Bundesliga in 1994-95 and 1995-96, the German Supercup in 1995 and 1996, and the European Champions League in 1997. Sammer was the German Footballer of the Year in 1995 and 1996 and became the

only Dortmund player to win the Ballon d'Or award in 1996.

6. Michael Lusch began his pro career with Dortmund in 1982 and didn't leave until 1993, when he headed to 1. FC Kaiserslautern. In between, he chipped in with a dozen goals and assists in 241 matches. with 203 of the appearances coming in the Bundesliga. He helped the team win the German Cup in 1988-89 and reach the UEFA Cup final in 1992-93. After hanging up his boots, he became an assistant manager and scout with Rot Weiss Essen.

7. German-born Turkish international midfielder Nuri Şahin launched his pro career with Dortmund from 2005 to 2011 before leaving for Real Madrid. He also had a loan spell with Feyenoord in Holland in 2007-08. In August 2005, he set a record at the time as the youngest ever player in the Bundesliga when he was 16 years and 334 days of age. Three months later, he became the youngest player to score in the Bundesliga at the time. Şahin won the league title in 2010-11 and was named the Bundesliga player of the season. He returned to Dortmund on loan in 2013-14 and remained until 2018, when he joined Werder Bremen and also won a German Cup and German Supercup with that team.

8. Miroslav "Mirko" Votava was a key player in Dortmund's midfield from 1974 to 1982 and helped them earn promotion to the Bundesliga in 1976. He left for Atlético Madrid in Spain and later returned to the Bundesliga with

Werder Bremen, where he played for another decade. With Dortmund, he played just under 300 games and netted 32 goals. Votava was born in Prague, in the former nation of Czechoslovakia, but he played five times with West Germany.

9. Attacking midfielder/forward Mario Götze enjoyed two stints with Dortmund, as he played from 2009 to 2013 to kick off his pro career and again from 2016 to 2020, when he left for the Dutch team PSV Eindhoven. In between his Dortmund days, he played with Bayern Munich. The German international won the Bundesliga with Dortmund in 2010-11 and 2011-12, along with the German Cup in 2011-12 and 2016-17 and the 2019 German Supercup. Götze played 158 times with the squad and posted 45 goals and 61 assists.

10. Another midfielder who began his pro journey with Dortmund was Marc-André Kruska. He joined in 1999 as a youth and made his first-team debut at the tender age of 17 in 2004-05. He left in 2009 to join Brugge in Belgium before returning to Germany to play with Energie Cottbus shortly afterward. He helped Dortmund reach the German Cup final in 2007-08 and was the gold winner of the Fritz Walter Medal for the best under-18 player in the Bundesliga. Kruska played just over 100 games with Dortmund and scored twice.

CHAPTER 7:

SENSATIONAL STRIKERS/FORWARDS

QUIZ TIME!

1. How many goals did Pierre-Emerick Aubameyang score in the 2016-17 Bundesliga?

   a. 22

   b. 27

   c. 31

   d. 34

2. Jakub Błaszczykowski recorded 15 Bundesliga assists in 2012-13.

   a. True

   b. False

3. Who scored 18 goals in the 2001-02 Bundesliga season?

   a. Ewerthon

   b. Márcio Amoroso

   c. Jan Koller

   d. Lars Ricken

4. How many assists did Thorgan Hazard record in 2019-20 domestic league matches?

    a. 13
    b. 14
    c. 15
    d. 16

5. Which forward received 8 yellow cards in the 1992-93 Bundesliga?

    a. Flemming Povlsen
    b. Jürgen Wegmann
    c. Lothar Sippel
    d. Frank Mill

6. How many assists did Lars Ricken earn in the 2002-03 Bundesliga season?

    a. 5
    b. 6
    c. 7
    d. 8

7. Tomáš Rosický recorded 14 assists in the 2001-02 Bundesliga season.

    a. True
    b. False

8. Who scored 17 goals in the 2019-20 Bundesliga season?

    a. Marco Reus
    b. Jadon Sancho
    c. Paco Alcácer
    d. Erling Håland

9. Which player notched 15 goals in the 1992-93 Bundesliga?

   a. Stéphane Chapuisat
   b. Flemming Povlsen
   c. Ulf Raschke
   d. Frank Mill

10. Which forward scored 16 goals in the 2013-14 Bundesliga season?

   a. Pierre-Emerick Aubameyang
   b. Henrikh Mkhitaryan
   c. Marco Reus
   d. Jonas Hofmann

11. Which player scored 6 goals from the penalty spot in the 2008-09 Bundesliga?

   a. Kevin-Prince Boateng
   b. Tamás Hajnal
   c. Alexander Frei
   d. Nelson Valdez

12. Robert Lewandowski scored 74 Bundesliga goals in his time with Dortmund.

   a. True
   b. False

13. Which player tallied 11 assists in 2016-17 domestic league games?

   a. Marco Reus
   b. Adrián Ramos
   c. Alexander Isak
   d. Ousmane Dembélé

14. How many goals did Erling Håland score in all competitions with Dortmund in 2019-20?

    a. 11
    b. 13
    c. 15
    d. 16

15. Who scored 19 goals to lead Dortmund in the 2009-10 Bundesliga season?

    a. Kevin Großkreutz
    b. Nelson Valdez
    c. Lucas Barrios
    d. Mohamed Zidan

16. Pierre-Emerick Aubameyang scored 162 goals in all competitions with Dortmund.

    a. True
    b. False

17. Which forward scored 15 goals in domestic league matches in the 2004-05 season?

    a. Euzebiusz Smolarek
    b. Tomáš Rosický
    c. Ewerthon
    d. Jan Koller

18. How many goals did Robert Lewandowski score in 2012-13 domestic league games?

    a. 23
    b. 24

c. 25

d. 26

19. Who was the only forward to be shown a red card in the 2017-18 domestic league?

    a. Pierre-Emerick Aubameyang

    b. Michy Batshuayi

    c. André Schürrle

    d. Jadon Sancho

20. Karl-Heinz Riedle and Heiko Herrlich both scored 7 goals in 1995-96 Bundesliga games.

    a. True

    b. False

QUIZ ANSWERS

1. C – 31

2. B – False

3. B – Márcio Amoroso

4. A – 13

5. D – Frank Mill

6. C – 7

7. B – False

8. B – Jadon Sancho

9. A – Stéphane Chapuisat

10. C – Marco Reus

11. C – Alexander Frei

12. A – True

13. D – Ousmane Dembélé

14. D – 16

15. C – Lucas Barrios

16. B – False

17. D – Jan Koller

18. B – 24

19. A – Pierre-Emerick Aubameyang

20. A – True

DID YOU KNOW?

1. One of the best-known strikers in the Bundesliga era was Polish international Robert Lewandowski, who played with Dortmund before leaving on a free transfer for Bayern Munich. Before departing, he notched 103 goals in 187 games between 2010 and 2014. He had already won a trio of Golden Boots in various Polish leagues and he won another with Dortmund in 2013-14 with 20 goals in 33 games. Oddly, this was his lowest total in three seasons as he tallied 24 and 22 league goals the previous two campaigns. Lewandowski also helped the club win two straight league titles, a German Cup, a German Supercup, and a runners-up medal from the 2012-13 European Champions League.

2. Striker Jan Koller scored consistently with Dortmund between 2001 and 2006, with 79 goals in 184 contests. The Czech Republic international began his pro career in his homeland and arrived in Germany from Belgian side Anderlecht. Koller actually played as a goalkeeper as a youth and this helped Dortmund in 2002-03 in a game against Bayern Munich. With keeper Jens Lehmann sent off during the second half and no substitutes left, Koller took his place in the 67th minute and didn't allow a goal even though his side was reduced to nine men due to an earlier expulsion.

3. After joining Dortmund from Borussia Mönchengladbach in 1995 and sharing the Bundesliga Golden Boot in his last season there with 20 goals, German international forward Heiko Herrlich helped Dortmund capture the Bundesliga title in 1995-96 and 2001-02, as well as the European Champions League and Intercontinental Cup in 1997. Along the way, Herrlich scored 56 goals in 183 matches with the side before retiring in 2004. He entered the world of football management several years later.

4. Ewerthon Henrique de Souza, simply known as Ewerthon, was a Brazilian international forward who was known for his long-range shooting, pace, and dribbling skills. He played with clubs all over the world, including Dortmund from 2001 to 2005, before leaving for Real Zaragoza in Spain. Ewerthon scored and set up another goal in his team debut and went on to contribute over 50 goals with the team in 154 outings. This helped them win the Bundesliga in 2001-02 and reach the UEFA Cup final the same season.

5. Argentine-born forward Lucas Barrios played nationally for Paraguay and was nicknamed "La Pantera" (The Panther) for his prowess in the 18-yard box. In fact, the IFFHS recognized him as the top scorer in the world for 2008 with 37 goals. Barrios has suited up for nearly 20 different teams in his career and enjoyed a stint with Dortmund from 2009 to 2012, with 49 goals in just over 100 matches. This included a goal in five straight league games in his first campaign with the club, in which he finished

with 19 league goals and 23 in all competitions. Barrios won league titles with Dortmund in 2010-11 and 2011-12 as well as the 2011-12 German Cup.

6. Another forward who netted 49 goals for Dortmund was Norbert Dickel, who managed the feat in 107 games between 1986 and 1990 before retiring. He had come over from 1. FC Köln where he won a runners-up medal in the UEFA Cup the previous season. With Dortmund, Dickel won the German Cup in 1988-89 and scored twice to help the team win its first major trophy since 1966. Dickel's career came to an end when he was just 28 due to injury and he then became stadium announcer and a radio broadcaster for the club.

7. German forward Michael Rummenigge was the younger brother of the legendary Karl-Heinz Rummenigge, the skipper of Bayern Munich Germany. Rummenigge played with his sibling at Bayern from 1982 to 1988, and then joined Dortmund until 1993 before heading to Japan to finish his career. He obviously wasn't that popular with some Dortmund fans when he joined from their rivals, but won them over by winning the German Cup in his first season, as well as the German Supercup in 1999. He also helped the team reach the final of the 1992-03 UEFA Cup and scored 45 times in 193 games with the side.

8. Between 1975 and 1981, forward Peter Geyer helped Dortmund earn promotion back to the Bundesliga and chipped in with 48 goals in 216 contests. The team finished

second in 2 Bundesliga in 1975-76 to gain promotion and five years later Geyer left for Eintracht Braunschweig. He notched 38 league goals for the side and was quite dependable in German Cup contests with 9 goals in 18 games.

9. Nicknamed "Kobra," Jürgen Wegmann played 138 times for Dortmund between 1984 and 1986 and again between 1987 and 1989, scoring 46 goals. He originally joined from Rot Weiss Essen and left for Schalke 04 two years later. Dortmund then reacquired him from Bayern Munich. During his two stints, Wegmann helped the side win the 1989 German Supercup and reach the final of the 1992-93 UEFA Cup.

10. One of the new breed of Dortmund players is English international winger Jadon Sancho, who joined the club in 2017 after spending his youth career with Watford and Manchester City. Sancho, who's the first Englishman to play for Dortmund, was still with the side as of January 2021 and had registered 40 goals in 121 matches. He once scored in seven straight games with Dortmund in 2019-20 and had a goal and assists in the team's 2019 German Supercup triumph. Sancho was named to the Bundesliga Team of the Season for 2018-19.

CHAPTER 8:

NOTABLE TRANSFERS/SIGNINGS

QUIZ TIME!

1. From which club did Dortmund acquire Marco Reus in 2012-13?

    a. Rott Weiss Ahlen

    b. Eintracht Frankfurt

    c. Borussia Mönchengladbach

    d. He was promoted from the youth team.

2. Robert Lewandowski was then the club's largest transfer fee received when he went to Bayern Munich for €75 million in 2014.

    a. True

    b. False

3. Dortmund acquired Erling Håland from which club in 2019-20?

    a. Molde FK

    b. RB Leipzig

    c. RB Salzburg

    d. SK Brann

4. Who did Dortmund sign from Shakhtar Donetsk in 2013-14?

    a. Andriy Yarmolenko
    b. Nuri Şahin
    c. Miloš Jojić
    d. Henrikh Mkhitaryan

5. How much did Dortmund reportedly pay to acquire 18-year-old Emre Mor in 2016-17?

    a. €1.5 million
    b. €2 million
    c. €6 million
    d. €9.75 million

6. Dortmund signed Pierre-Emerick Aubameyang from which French club in 2013-14?

    a. AS Saint-Étienne
    b. LOSC Lille
    c. AC Milan
    d. Dijon FCO

7. Dortmund transferred Shinji Kagawa to Manchester City for a fee of £18 million in 2012-13.

    a. True
    b. False

8. From which club did Dortmund acquire Matthias Sammer from in 1992-93?

    a. Dynamo Dresden
    b. VfB Stuttgart

c. Inter Milan

d. Juventus

9. How much did Dortmund reportedly pay to acquire Robert Lewandowski from Lech Poznań in 2010-11?

    a. €3.5 million

    b. €4 million

    c. €4.75 million

    d. €5 million

10. What club did keeper Wolfgang de Beer play for before joining Dortmund?

    a. MSV Duisburg

    b. Rangers FC

    c. Mönchengladbach

    d. Arminia Bielefeld

11. Which club did Dortmund sell Ousmane Dembélé to in 2017?

    a. Manchester United

    b. Inter Milan

    c. Paris Saint-Germain

    d. FC Barcelona

12. Dortmund paid a reported transfer fee of €30.5 million for Mats Hummels in 2019-20.

    a. True

    b. False

13. Dortmund acquired which player from KFC Uerdingen 05 in 1991-92?

a. Flemming Povlsen

b. Knut Reinhart

c. Bodo Schmidt

d. Stéphane Chapuisat

14. Which keeper did Dortmund sign from 1.FC Kaiserslautern in 2002-03?

a. Roman Weidenfeller

b. Guillaume Warmuz

c. Philipp Laux

d. Dennis Gentenaar

15. Who did Dortmund sign from TSV 1860 Munich II in 2015-16 for a steal at €2.5 million?

a. Roman Bürki

b. Jakub Błaszczykowski

c. Julian Weigl

d. Ju-ho Park

16. Dortmund brought in keeper Stefan Klos on a free transfer from Eintracht Dortmund's youth team.

a. True

b. False

17. How much did Dortmund pay for Andriy Yarmolenko in one of the club's biggest misses on the transfer market in 2017?

a. €30 million

b. €25 million

c. €24 million

d. €21.5 million

18. Who did Dortmund acquire from Paris Saint-Germain in 1999-2000?

    a. Otto Addo
    b. Christian Wörns
    c. Victor Ikpeba
    d. Evanilson

19. From which club did Dortmund sign Shinji Kagawa from in 2011-12?

    a. Gamba Osaka
    b. FC Tokyo
    c. Cerezo Osaka
    d. Kashima Antlers

20. Dortmund signed Erling Håland for a fee of €20 million in 2019-20.

    a. True
    b. False

QUIZ ANSWERS

1. C – Borussia Mönchengladbach

2. B – False

3. C – RB Salzburg

4. D – Henrikh Mkhitaryan

5. D – €9.75 million

6. A – AS Saint-Étienne

7. B – False

8. C – Inter Milan

9. C – €4.75 million

10. A – MSV Duisburg

11. D – FC Barcelona

12. A – True

13. D – Stéphane Chapuisat

14. A – Roman Weidenfeller

15. C – Julian Weigl

16. A – True

17. B – €25 million

18. B – Christian Wörns

19. C – Cerezo Osaka

20. A – True

DID YOU KNOW?

1. There's a significant difference in Dortmund's record transfer fee when it comes to received and paid. The club received a reported €130 million for winger Ousmane Dembélé when he was sold to Barcelona in the summer of 2017. Meanwhile, the record fee paid for a player was just a reported €30.5 million for defender and former captain Mats Hummels from Bayern Munich in 2019.

2. In January 2008, Mats Hummels was acquired by Dortmund on loan from Bayern Munich, and then signed permanently by the club for a fee of €4.2 million. He was then the club's acting captain from 2014 to 2016 before rejoining Bayern in the summer of 2016, for a reported €35 million. Dortmund then reacquired Hummels for a club-record transfer fee of €30.5 million in June 2019.

3. Another Dortmund player who spent time with Dortmund and Bayern Munich was Mario Götze. The German international attacker began his pro career with Dortmund from 2009 to 2013. However, in April 2013, Bayern put in a €37 million bid that triggered a release clause in his contract. At the time, the transaction made Götze the second-costliest German player next to Mesut Özil. Dortmund then paid a reported €22 million to reacquire his services from Bayern in July 2016. Götze left the club on a free transfer to join PSV Eindhoven in Holland in October 2020.

4. German international Kevin Großkreutz played with Dortmund from 2009 to 2015 but was demoted to Borussia Dortmund II near the end of his contract. He was sold to Galatasaray of Turkey in September 2015 but the transaction wasn't officially registered before the transfer window closed. FIFA voided the transfer, which meant Großkreutz wasn't able to play for anybody until January 1St, 2016. He then signed with Galatasaray for a fee of €1.5 million. Just 15 days after joining Galatasaray, Großkreutz was sold to VfB Stuttgart for approximately €2.2 million. Just over a year later, his contract was mutually terminated after Großkreutz was involved in a bar fight.

5. In July 2013, Gabon international forward Pierre-Emerick Aubameyang was bought from Saint-Étienne of France for a reported €13 million. He helped Dortmund win a pair of German Supercups and a German Cup, as well as winning several individual honors and the Bundesliga Golden Boot in 2016-17 with 31 goals in 32 games. He was then sold to English Premier League side Arsenal in January 2018 for an estimated €63.75 million, which was a club record for both teams at the time. This made Aubameyang the most expensive Gabonese player of all time.

6. Dortmund paid a reported €25 million to Dynamo Kyiv for Ukrainian international forward Andriy Yarmolenko in August 2017 after nine seasons with the club. With Kyiv, Yarmolenko scored over 135 goals in more than 300 appearances but his career stalled at Signal Iduna Park as he played just 26 times for the club and chipped in with 6

goals, before being sold to West Ham United of the English Premier League in July 2018 for a reported €20 million. Yarmolenko's career also hit a roadblock in England, mainly due to injuries.

7. Versatile German international midfielder/defender Emre Can was another player who cost Dortmund €25 million when he was picked up from Italian giants Juventus in January 2020. The former Bayern Munich player was originally acquired by Dortmund on loan with the move, which was made permanent shortly afterward. Can scored in his Dortmund debut, which was one of two he scored in 15 outings with the club in his first season. He then scored once in his first 10 league games in 2020-21.

8. Brazilian international forward Márcio Amoroso played with more than a dozen pro teams between 1992 and 2016, with a stint at Dortmund from 2001 to 2004. He was bought for a reported €25.5 million from AC Parma of Italy in 2001, which was quite a lot of money back then. Amoroso was a hit in his first season, with 26 goals in 46 games as the club won the Bundesliga title, and he won the Golden Boot with 18 goals. His output dipped to 9 goals in 35 outings the next campaign. However, he played just nine games in 2003-04 but scored 8 goals. Amoroso then joined Malaga of Spain as a free agent and didn't hang up his boots until 2017, when he was 45 years old.

9. Although his older brother Eden Hazard is regarded as one of the best players in the world, Thorgan Hazard didn't come cheap when Bayern bought him from Borussia Mönchengladbach in May 2019. The Belgian international attacker was acquired for a reported €25.5 million and he chipped in with 7 league goals in 33 appearances in his first season, with no goals in 10 domestic and European Cup contests. Hazard then kicked off the 2020-21 campaign with 3 goals in his first 12 outings.

10. French center-back Abdou Diallo was bought from fellow Bundesliga side Mainz 05 in June 2018 for a reported €28 million to help shore up the team's defense. He appeared in 28 league games and 38 matches overall that season, chipping in with 1 goal. Dortmund made a quick €4 million profit, though, as Diallo was sold to French side Paris Saint-Germain just 13 months later for a reported €32 million. With PSG, Diallo had won a league title, a French Cup a French League Cup, two Trophée des Champions, and a European Champions League runners-up medal by the end of 2019-20.

CHAPTER 9:

ODDS & ENDS

QUIZ TIME!

1. Who scored Dortmund's first goal in the Bundesliga?

    a. Wilhelm Sturm
    b. Franz Brungs
    c. Hans-Jürgen Kurrat
    d. Friedhelm Konietzka

2. After his soccer career, Manfred Burgsmüller joined the Rhein Fire of the NFL Europe league as a kicker, becoming the oldest league player at the age of 52.

    a. True
    b. False

3. Who was the youngest player to make his Dortmund debut, at the age of 16 years and 1 day old?

    a. Nuri Şahin
    b. Ibrahim Tanko
    c. Youssoufa Moukoko
    d. Gio Reyna

4. How many matches did Dortmund win in its first Bundesliga season?

    a. 10
    b. 12
    c. 14
    d. 15

5. After Dortmund's success in the 2012-13 UEFA Champions League, they began averaging 1,000 fans from which nation at home games?

    a. Denmark
    b. United Kingdom
    c. Switzerland
    d. America

6. How many wins did Dortmund register in the 1994-95 Bundesliga season?

    a. 23
    b. 22
    c. 21
    d. 20

7. Pierre-Emerick Aubameyang became the third player in Bundesliga history to score a hat trick in a top-flight debut.

    a. True
    b. False

8. How many wins did Dortmund post in 1971-72, the year the club was relegated?

    a. 9
    b. 8

c. 7

d. 6

9. The rivalry known as "the Revierderby" is between Dortmund and which other team?

   a. Bayer Leverkusen

   b. FC Schalke 04

   c. Werder Bremen

   d. FC Augsburg

10. Which team handed Dortmund their biggest loss in the Bundesliga, a 12 0 drubbing in 1977-78?

    a. Bayern Munich

    b. Borussia Mönchengladbach

    c. VfL Wolfsburg

    d. Hertha Berlin

11. Who was the oldest player to make an appearance for Dortmund, at the age of 42 years and 44 days?

    a. Roman Weidenfeller

    b. Alfred Kelbassa

    c. Toni Schumacher

    d. Adi Preißler

12. Paco Alcácer set the record for most goals scored by a substitute in the 2018-19 Bundesliga.

    a. True

    b. False

13. In Dortmund's first Bundesliga season, how many matches did they draw?

a. 3

b. 4

c. 5

d. 6

14. Paco Alcácer scored how many Bundesliga goals as a substitute in 2018-19?

a. 10

b. 11

c. 12

d. 13

15. How many goals did Dortmund tally in its first Bundesliga season?

a. 54

b. 73

c. 82

d. 91

16. As of 2020, the most wins Dortmund posted in one Bundesliga season is 24.

a. True

b. False

17. Which is not one of Dortmund's nicknames?

a. Die Borussen

b. Der BVB

c. The Black and Yellows

d. Der Stripes

18. What is the fewest goals Dortmund has allowed in a Bundesliga season as of 2020?

    a. 4
    b. 13
    c. 22
    d. 31

19. What is the most points Dortmund has recorded in a Bundesliga campaign as of 2020?

    a. 75
    b. 78
    c. 81
    d. 83

20. Dortmund won 22 matches to win promotion from the 2. Bundesliga in the season of 1975-76.

    a. True
    b. False

QUIZ ANSWERS

1. D – Friedhelm Konietzka

2. A – True

3. C – Youssoufa Moukoko

4. C – 14

5. B – United Kingdom

6. D – 20

7. A – True

8. D – 6

9. B – FC Schalke 04

10. B – Borussia Mönchengladbach

11. C – Toni Schumacher

12. A – True

13. C – 5

14. A – 12

15. B – 73

16. B – False

17. D – Der Stripes

18. C – 22

19. C – 81

20. A – True

DID YOU KNOW?

1. The club wasn't financially stable during the 1970s and the team was relegated from the Bundesliga after the 1971-72 season. They moved into the city-owned Westfalenstadion in 1974 and earned promotion back into the Bundesliga two years later. The club eventually bought the ground. Dortmund continued to have financial problems through the 1980s, escaping relegation in 1985-1986 by emerging victorious from a third decisive playoff match against Fortuna Köln following their 16th-place finish in the regular season.

2. In October 2000, Borussia Dortmund became the first publicly traded soccer club on the German stock market. The club's fortunes began to decline for several years, though, and it sold the Westfalenstadion to a real estate trust to help reduce the debt. In 2003, rivals Bayern Munich loaned Dortmund €2 million to help cover the club's payroll. Two years after that, the club came close to bankruptcy again when its shares sank in value by 80 percent on the Frankfurt Stock Exchange.

3. To help with Dortmund's financial problems, Hans-Joachim Watzke took over as CEO and all players took a pay cut of 20 percent. Also, in December 2005, the naming rights to the Westfalenstadion were sold to an insurance company and the stadium will be officially known as

"Signal Iduna Park" until sometime in 2021. The club also reacquired ownership of the venue in 2006, thanks to a loan from the Morgan Stanley investment banking company.

4. The Signal Iduna Park stadium is currently the largest football ground in Germany, with a capacity of 81,365, and Borussia Dortmund typically boasts one of the highest average attendances of any soccer club on the planet. The stadium was used under its original name for the 1974 FIFA World Cup but it was named the "FIFA World Cup Stadium, Dortmund" for the tournament in 2006 because Signal Iduna wasn't a sponsor of FIFA. The Signal Iduna name also isn't allowed to be officially used when hosting UEFA events.

5. Since 2006, Signal Iduna Park has hosted a historical museum about the club, known as Borusseum. In addition, in 2011 the team partnered with a company called Hanwha Q Cells Co., Ltd., which installed 8,768 solar cells on the stadium roof. The cells can generate approximately 860,000 kWh of power a year. The stadium typically sees numerous British fans at each Dortmund home game because the cost of tickets is considerably lower than for most Premier League contests.

6. Before moving into the Westfalenstadion in 1974 to accommodate the growing number of fans, Dortmund played at the Stadion Rote Erde, which is located just next door. This ground is now the home of Borussia Dortmund

II. The stadium was completed in 1926 and Borussia Dortmund moved in as a tenant in 1937. The maximum capacity at its peak for soccer games was 42,000 and it now holds 10,000 for Borussia Dortmund II and 25,000 for track and field events.

7. Dortmund's first regular home ground was the Weiße Wiese (The White Field), with a capacity of 18,000. The venue was also known as the Borussia Sportpark and was located in the north of the city. The club left the stadium in 1937 because it was needed by a local factory to help prepare for World War II and the expansion of the Nazi movement.

8. On Sept. 8, 1913, Borussia Dortmund played a home game against VfB Dortmund and came away with a 1-0 victory. However, celebrations didn't last long because several opposing players complained to the referee that one of the goals was smaller than the other. Somebody borrowed a tape measure from a nearby farmer and the referee then proceeded to measure both goals. It turned out that one was approximately nine inches smaller than the other and the result was wiped from the local league's record books.

9. The training ground and base for the club's academy, named Hohenbuschei, sits in the Brackel section of the city. The complex contains physical exercise and rehabilitation robotics areas, massage and physiotherapy rooms, hydrotherapy pools, steam and sauna rooms, weight training, conference halls, classrooms, a restaurant,

TV studio, and offices. There are five grass pitches, two of which have under-soil heating, along with an artificial turf pitch, three smaller grass pitches, and a multi-functional sports arena.

10. The 1963-64 season was the launch of the Bundesliga. Dortmund placed fourth on the league table, with their home games being played at Stadion Rote Erde. They also fared relatively well in Europe, as they reached the semifinal of the European Cup but were eliminated by Inter Milan. Friedhelm Konietzka led the club in goals in the league and overall, with 20 Bundesliga markers and 24 in all competitions.

CHAPTER 10:

DOMESTIC COMPETITION

QUIZ TIME!

1. How many times has Dortmund been runners-up in the German League Championship as of 2020?

    a. 7

    b. 8

    c. 9

    d. 10

2. Dortmund won its first German Championship in 1949.

    a. True

    b. False

3. Which year did Dortmund make its only appearance in the League Cup (DFL-Ligapokal) Final?

    a. 1997

    b. 1999

    c. 2003

    d. 2006

4. How many times has Dortmund won the German Supercup (DFB Super Cup) as of 2020?

    a. 7
    b. 6
    c. 5
    d. 4

5. Who did Dortmund defeat to win their first DFB Super Cup in 1989?

    a. VfB Stuttgart
    b. 1. FC Kaiserslautern
    c. FC Schalke 04
    d. Bayern Munich

6. How many times has Dortmund won the German League Championship as of 2020?

    a. 7
    b. 8
    c. 9
    d. 10

7. Dortmund won the Oberliga West division in three consecutive seasons, from 1947 to 1950.

    a. True
    b. False

8. When did Dortmund win its first league title of the Bundesliga era?

    a. 1994-95
    b. 1995-96

c. 2001-02

d. 2002-03

9. Who did Dortmund lose to in the DFB-Ligapokal final?

a. 1. FC Kaiserslautern

b. VfL Wolfsburg

c. 1. FC Koln

d. Hamburger SV

10. Which year did Dortmund win its first German Championship?

a. 1944

b. 1952

c. 1956

d. 1959

11. How many points did Dortmund register when winning its first Bundesliga title?

a. 42

b. 47

c. 49

d. 68

12. Dortmund and Bayern Munich have played each other in the DFB Super Cup final five times as of 2020.

a. True

b. False

13. When did Dortmund first reach the final of the DFB-Ligapokal?

a. 1989

b. 1990

c. 1995

d. 1996

14. How many of Dortmund's eight league titles did the club win in the Bundesliga era, as of 2020?

    a. 6

    b. 5

    c. 4

    d. 3

15. As of 2020, how many times has Dortmund won the German Cup (DFB Cup)?

    a. 2

    b. 3

    c. 4

    d. 5

16. Dortmund has won two Bundesliga/German Cup doubles as of 2020.

    a. True

    b. False

17. Which club did Dortmund defeat 2-0 to win the 1964-65 DFB Cup final?

    a. Alemannia Aachen

    b. FC Schalke 04

    c. 1. FC Nürnberg

    d. Hannover 96

18. How many domestic league/cup trophies has Dortmund won as of 2020?

    a. 14

    b. 16

    c. 17

    d. 18

19. Who did Dortmund defeat in the 2016-17 DFB Cup final?

    a. Eintracht Frankfurt

    b. Borussia Mönchengladbach

    c. Bayern Munich

    d. Werder Bremen

20. Dortmund has been runners-up in the DFB Super Cup six times as of 2020.

    a. True

    b. False

QUIZ ANSWERS

1. C – 9

2. B – False

3. C – 2003

4. B – 6

5. D – Bayern Munich

6. B – 8

7. A – True

8. A – 1994-95

9. D – Hamburger SV

10. C – 1956

11. C – 49

12. B – False

13. A – 1989

14. B – 5

15. C – 4

16. B – False

17. A – Alemannia Aachen

18. D – 18

19. A – Eintracht Frankfurt

20. B – False

DID YOU KNOW?

1. Since being formed in 1909, Borussia Dortmund has won eight German Championship Bundesliga titles as of 2019-20 and has finished as runners-up in the league nine times. They were relegated from the Bundesliga in 1971-72 and earned promotion back to the Bundesliga from 2. Bundesliga North by finishing as the league's runners-up in 1975-76.

2. Dortmund has captured the German Cup (DFB-Pokal) four times as of 2019-20 and also finished as runners-up on five occasions. The club has also captured the German Supercup (DFB/DFL-Supercup) six times and finished as runners-up five times. In addition, Dortmund finished as runners-up in the now-defunct German League Cup (DFB-Ligapokal) on one occasion, in 2003.

3. The club won the German Championship/Bundesliga in 1956, 1957, 1963, 1994-95, 1995-96, 2001-02, 2010-11, and 2011-12, while finishing as runners-up in 1949, 1961, 1965-66, 1991-92, 2012-13, 2013-14, 2015-16, 2018-19, and 2019-20. They captured the German Cup (DFB-Pokal) in 1964-65, 1988-89, 2011-12, and 2016-17, while placing as runners-up in: 1962-63, 2007-08, 2013-14, 2014-15, and 2015-16. Their German Supercup (DFB/DFL-Supercup) triumphs took place in 1989, 1995, 1996, 2013, 2014, and 2019, while they were runners-up in 2011, 2012, 2016, 2017, and 2020.

4. Before the Bundesliga was formed in 1963-64, Dortmund had won several regional league titles. This includes a record six times in the Oberliga West/West German Championship, which they won in 1947-48, 1948-49, 1949-50, 1952-53, 1955-56, and 1956-57. They also finished as runners-up in 1960-61 and 1962-63. In addition, the club hoisted the Westphalia Cup in 1947.

5. Former captain Michael Zorc holds the club record for most appearances at 572. Goalkeeper Roman Weidenfeller is next at 453 games and midfielder Stefan Reuter is third with 421 appearances. The only other player to play over 500 games with the club as of January 2021 was midfielder Lars Ricken, who appeared 407 times; defender Dedé comes close at 398. There were also several players on the 2020-21 club who were within 30 games of reaching the 400-match plateau.

6. The youngest Borussia Dortmund player in the Bundesliga was Youssoufa Moukoko, who was 16 years and 1 day old. Moukoko was also the youngest to play for the club in the European Champions League when he was 16 years and 18 days of age. In addition, Moukoko was the youngest goal-scorer in Dortmund and Bundesliga history when he hit the back of the net on Dec. 18Th, 2020, at the age of 16 years and 28 days.

7. Dortmund made history on April 28, 1978, by suffering the worst loss in the history of the Bundesliga when they were trounced 12-0 by Borussia Mönchengladbach. The club

also played in the most undisciplined game ever in the Bundesliga, when a combined 15 cards were produced in their clash against Bayern Munich on April 7, 2001. However, Dortmund received just three of the cards. The most penalty kicks handed out in a Bundesliga encounter came on Nov. 9, 1965, when five of them were awarded during the Dortmund vs Borussia Mönchengladbach fixture.

8. The most red cards earned in Dortmund history was three, with several players sharing the career record. They were goalkeepers Roman Weidenfeller and Jens Lehmann and defenders Dedé and Michael Schulz. Lehmann was also sent off twice with a second yellow card while Dedé was sent off once with two yellow cards.

9. The club record for career red cards belongs to former midfielder and skipper Michael Zorc with 85 and he's followed by midfielder Stefan Reuter at 83 and defender Dedé with 66. Reuter holds the record for most second yellow cards in their Dortmund career with four while midfielder Tomáš Rosický and defender Matthias Sammer both received three. However, none of these three players received a straight red card while playing with the team.

10. Dortmund's most embarrassing defeats in the German Cup came in the very first round in the 1990-91 campaign when they were downed 3-1 away by SpVgg Fürth and in 1996-97 when they were edged 4-3 away in extra time by SG Wattenscheid. They were also beaten in the third

round in 1997-98 when they were dropped 2-1 by Eintracht Trier. These opponents were all regarded as amateur clubs when the games took place.

CHAPTER 11:

EUROPE AND BEYOND

QUIZ TIME!

1. How many international titles has Dortmund won as of 2020?

    a. 2

    b. 3

    c. 4

    d. 5

2. Dortmund first entered the European Cup competition in 1956-57.

    a. True

    b. False

3. Which team did Dortmund defeat in the 1996-97 UEFA Champions League final?

    a. Manchester United

    b. Ajax

    c. Juventus

    d. AC Milan

4. Which year did Dortmund reach the Intercontinental Cup Final for the first time?

    a. 1985
    b. 1990
    c. 1997
    d. 1999

5. How many times has Dortmund finished as runners-up in the UEFA Champions League as of 2020?

    a. 4
    b. 3
    c. 2
    d. 1

6. Which club did Dortmund defeat to win their first Intercontinental Cup?

    a. Cruzeiro EC
    b. Sporting CP
    c. Guarani FC
    d. Bangu AC

7. Dortmund won the European Cup Winners' Cup the first year they competed for it.

    a. True
    b. False

8. Who did Dortmund defeat in the 1965-66 European Cup Winners' Cup final?

    a. 1. FC Magdeburg
    b. Atlético Madrid

c. Dynamo Kyiv

d. Liverpool

9. Which player scored the winning goal in the 1965-66 European Cup Winners' Cup Final?

   a. Lothar Emmerich

   b. Reinhard Libuda

   c. Aki Schmidt

   d. Sigfried Held

10. Who scored the winning goal in the1997 Intercontinental Cup?

    a. Scott Booth

    b. Paulo Sousa

    c. Michael Zorc

    d. Heiko Herrlich

11. Which fellow German club defeated Dortmund in the 2012-13 UEFA Champions League final?

    a. 1. FC Kaiserslautern

    b. VfB Stuttgart

    c. Bayern Munich

    d. Arminia Bielefeld

12. In 2013-14, Dortmund ended Real Madrid's streak of 34 consecutive games with a goal scored in the European Champions League.

    a. True

    b. False

13. How many times has Dortmund reached the final round of the UEFA Cup as of 2020?

    a. 4

    b. 3

    c. 2

    d. 1

14. Which year did Dortmund reach the UEFA Cup final for the first time?

    a. 1990-91

    b. 1992-93

    c. 2002-03

    d. 2003-04

15. Which team defeated Dortmund in the 2001-02 UEFA Cup final?

    a. Feyenoord

    b. Grasshoppers CZ

    c. FC Bordeaux

    d. Inter Milan

16. Dortmund beat A.J. Auxerre in the semi-finals of the 1996-97 European Champions League.

    a. True

    b. False

17. Who defeated Dortmund in the 1997 UEFA Super Cup?

    a. Bayern Munich

    b. FC Barcelona

    c. Paris Saint-Germain

    d. Lyon

18. Which side did Dortmund not play against on their way to the 1992-93 UEFA Cup final?

    a. Paris Saint-Germain
    b. Floriana
    c. Real Zaragoza
    d. A.J. Auxerre

19. Which Dortmund player was tied for third place in goals scored in the 2001-02 UEFA Cup tournament?

    a. Lars Ricken
    b. Ewerthon
    c. Márcio Amoroso
    d. Jan Koller

20. Dortmund's Karl-Heinz Riedle was the top scorer in the 1996-97 UEFA Champions League with 5 goals.

    a. True
    b. False

QUIZ ANSWERS

1. B – 3

2. A – True

3. C – Juventus

4. C – 1997

5. D – 1

6. A – Cruzeiro EC

7. A – True

8. D – Liverpool

9. B – Reinhard Libuda

10. C – Michael Zorc

11. C – Bayern Munich

12. A – True

13. C – 2

14. B – 1992-93

15. A – Feyenoord

16. B – False

17. B – FC Barcelona

18. A – Paris Saint-Germain

19. C – Márcio Amoroso

20. B – False

DID YOU KNOW?

1. When it comes to Europe and beyond as of 2020, Borussia Dortmund has won the European Champions League once and finished as runners-up once. The club also captured the UEFA/European Cup Winners' Cup once while finishing as runners-up on two occasions. Dortmund won an Intercontinental Cup once and finished once as runners-up in the UEFA Super Cup.

2. Dortmund won the European Champions League in 1996-97 and finished as runners-up in 2012-13. Their UEFA/European Cup Winners' Cup victory was in 1965-66 and they were runners-up in 1992-93 and 2001-02. The Intercontinental Cup triumph came in 1997 and they were UEFA Super Cup runners-up the same year.

3. As of January 2021, the record for goals scored in a European Champions League match is 12. This took place in the 2016-17 campaign when Dortmund hammered Legia Warsaw of Poland 8–4. The top Dortmund career goal-scorer in the competition is Marco Reus and Robert Lewandowski with 17 each, followed by Pierre-Emerick Aubameyang, who tallied 15.

4. There have been just 17 penalty kicks taken in European Cup/Champions League Finals, with 12 of them being successful. One of these was taken by Dortmund's İlkay Gündoğan in the 68th minute of the 2012-13 match to level

the score 1-1 against rivals Bayern Munich in Munich. However, Arjen Robben scored the winner in the 89th minute at Wembley Stadium in London, England as Bayern took the trophy by a score of 2-1. This was one of just seven finals that have featured opponents from the same country.

5. Dortmund played the role of spoiler in the 2013-14 European Champions League, when Real Madrid was in the midst of a record consecutive goal-scoring streak in the competition at 34 straight games. Real's run began in the semifinal of the 2010-11 campaign and was eventually halted when Dortmund beat them 2-0 in Germany in the second leg of the quarterfinals in April 2014. Real Madrid's record was equaled by Paris Saint-Germain in August 2020.

6. Unfortunately, Dortmund is in the record book for the wrong reason where the UEFA Cup/Europa League is concerned. They were beaten 6-1 on aggregate in the 1992-93 Final by Juventus of Italy. They were beaten 3-1 at home in the first leg and then blanked 3-0 away in the deciding leg. The two teams met again in the 1996-07 European Champions League Final and Dortmund gained revenge with a 3-1 victory in Munich, Germany.

7. The UEFA Cup Winners' Cup was christened in 1960 and the last match was contested in 1999. It was originally known as the European Cup Winners' Cup; the name was changed in 1994. Dortmund reached the final in this

competition in 1965-66. It turned out to be a successful venture, as they beat English side Liverpool 2-1 in extra time, thanks to a goal by Reinhard Libuda in the 107th minute. Sigfried Held had given Dortmund the lead in the 61st minute at Hampden Park in Glasgow, Scotland while Roger Hunt equalized for Liverpool seven minutes later.

8. The UEFA Super Cup is a yearly contest featuring the winners of the European Champions League and the Europa League and was originally known as the European Super Cup until 1994. Between 1972 and 1999, the game was between the winners of the European Cup/UEFA Champions League and the UEFA Cup Winners' Cup. Dortmund played in the 1997 final because they were reigning Champions League winners and faced off against Barcelona of Spain. However, they lost the two-legged competition by losing 2-0 in Spain and drawing 1-1 at home.

9. The 2001-02 UEFA Cup final in Rotterdam, Holland, was contested between Dutch side Feyenoord and Dortmund. The Bundesliga club trailed 2-0 after 40 minutes before Márcio Amoroso pulled a goal back in the 47th minute when he converted a penalty kick. Feyenoord regained their two-goal lead just three minutes later, though, with Jan Koller scoring for Dortmund eight minutes after that. All 5 goals came within a 25-minute span from the 33rd to 58th minutes, as Feyenoord hung on for a 3-2 victory.

10. Dortmund's lone success outside of Europe came in the 1997 Intercontinental Cup, which ran from 1960 to 2004.

They took on Cruzeiro of Brazil and came out on top 2-0 in Tokyo, Japan, courtesy of goals by Michael Zorc in the 34th minute and Heiko Herrlich in the 85th. The Intercontinental Cup was also known as the European/South American Cup and then the Toyota Cup between 1980 and 2004. The game was operated by UEFA and CONMEBOL and it featured a club from each football confederation. These were typically the European Champions League winners against the winners of the South American Copa Libertadores.

CHAPTER 12:

TOP SCORERS

QUIZ TIME!

1. Who is Dortmund's all-time goal-scorer in all competitions as of 2020?

    a. Manfred Burgsmüller

    b. Michael Zorc

    c. Lothar Emmerich

    d. Alfred Preissler

2. Friedhelm Konietzka led Dortmund in scoring in the club's first season in the Bundesliga.

    a. True

    b. False

3. Which player led Dortmund in scoring in the Oberliga West for four consecutive seasons?

    a. Jürgen Schütz

    b. Alfred Kelbassa

    c. Franze Farke

    d. Alfred Schmidt

4. Who led Dortmund and the Bundesliga in scoring in the 2013-14 season?

    a. Jakub Błaszczykowski

    b. Marco Reus

    c. Robert Lewandowski

    d. Márcio Amoroso

5. Which player led Dortmund in scoring in the Bundesliga from 1991 to 1994?

    a. Norbert Dickel

    b. Michael Zorc

    c. Stéphane Chapuisat

    d. Michael Rummenigge

6. How many goals did Alfred Preissler score across his two stints with Dortmund?

    a. 177

    b. 174

    c. 168

    d. 157

7. Lothar Emmerich was the first player on Dortmund to lead the Bundesliga in scoring in 1965-66.

    a. True

    b. False

8. Which player never led the Bundesliga in scoring while playing for Dortmund?

    a. Pierre-Emerick Aubameyeng

    b. Manfred Burgsmüller

c. Robert Lewandowski

d. Lothar Emmerich

9. How many seasons did Pierre-Emerick Aubameyeng lead Dortmund in scoring in the Bundesliga?

   a. 4

   b. 3

   c. 2

   d. 1

10. Which player ranks third in all-time scoring for Dortmund in all competitions as of 2020?

    a. Jürgen Schütz

    b. Lothar Emmerich

    c. Friedhelm Konietzka

    d. Michael Zorc

11. How many goals did Lothar Emmerich score in the 1965-66 Bundesliga season?

    a. 26

    b. 28

    c. 29

    d. 31

12. As of 2020, six different Dortmund players have led the Bundesliga in scoring.

    a. True

    b. False

13. How many goals did Friedhelm Konietzka score in the 1963-64 Bundesliga season?

a. 22

b. 21

c. 20

d. 19

14. This player was Dortmund's top goal-scorer in the 1999-00 Bundesliga season with only 7 goals.

   a. Lars Ricken

   b. Giuseppe Reina

   c. Fredi Bobic

   d. Heiko Herrlich

15. How many goals did Manfred Burgsmüller score to lead the club in the 1980-81 Bundesliga season?

   a. 19

   b. 20

   c. 25

   d. 27

16. Pierre-Emerick Aubameyang's 31 goals in the 2016-17 Bundesliga set the record for most goals by a non-German player.

   a. True

   b. False

17. Which two players were tied with 16 goals each in the 2003-04 Bundesliga season?

   a. Jan Koller and Ewerthon

   b. Dedé and David Odonkor

   c. Jan Koller and Tomáš Rosický

   d. Torsten Frings and Ewerthon

18. In how many Bundesliga seasons did Manfred Burgsmüller lead Dortmund in scoring?

    a. 4
    b. 5
    c. 6
    d. 7

19. Which player led Dortmund with 18 goals in the 2018-19 Bundesliga season?

    a. Jadon Sancho
    b. Paco Alcácer
    c. Marco Reus
    d. Axel Witsel

20. Marco Reus has led Dortmund in scoring in the Bundesliga on two separate occasions as of 2020.

    a. True
    b. False

QUIZ ANSWERS

1. D – Alfred Preissler

2. A – True

3. A – Jürgen Schütz

4. C – Robert Lewandowski

5. C – Stéphane Chapuisat

6. B – 174

7. A – True

8. B – Manfred Burgsmüller

9. A – 4

10. D – Michael Zorc

11. D – 31

12. B – False

13. C – 20

14. C – Fredi Bobic

15. D – 27

16. A – True

17. A – Jan Koller and Ewerthon

18. C – 6

19. B – Paco Alcácer

20. B – False

DID YOU KNOW?

1. Although Adi Preißler (Alfred Preissler) played up front with Dortmund before the Bundesliga era and records are hard to verify, it's widely believed that he's the club's all-time leading marksman with 174 goals in just over 250 games. Preissler had two stints with the team. He played from 1946 to 1950 before leaving for Preußen Münster for a season and then returning from 1961 to 1959. He also helped the side win back-to-back German championships in 1956 and 1957 and played twice nationally for West Germany. Preissler went into football management after retiring.

2. Michael Zorc, who was the team's longest-serving skipper from 1989 to 1998, was also its leading scorer in the Bundesliga era, hammering home159 goals for the side in 572 appearances. The German international midfielder played his entire pro career with the club from 1981 to 1998 and his 463 Bundesliga appearances is the team record. Zorc netted 131 league goals, with many of them coming on penalty kicks, which he was an expert at. After retiring, he became the club's sports manager.

3. Center-forward Manfred Burgsmüller scored 158 times for the black and yellow in just 252 matches between 1976 and 1983, which means he tallied .63 goals-per-game. The former club captain notched 135 league goals for the club

and, even though he was sometimes employed as a midfielder, he scored at least 15 goals in each of his Bundesliga campaigns. Burgsmüller scored over 300 club goals with several teams during his career and, after hanging up his boots, was an NFL Europe league kicker from 1996 to 2002 for the Rhein Fire, playing until a record age of 52.

4. Currently Ranking fourth on the club's all-time scoring list is German international forward Lothar Emmerich, with 148 goals in 249 outings. He started his pro career with the team from 1960 to 1969, helping them earn passage to the Bundesliga in 1963. Emmerich scored 126 league goals and also helped the squad capture the German Cup in 1964-65 and the European Cup Winners' Cup the very next season. In addition, Emmerich won the Bundesliga Golden Boot in 1965-66 and 1966-67.

5. Of Dortmund's top-10 all-time scorers, forward Friedhelm "Timo" Konietzka had the best strike rate per-match, scoring .76 goals-per-game. He found the back of the net 145 times in 191 outings with the German international, being runner-up for the Bundesliga Golden Boot for three straight seasons, starting in 1963-64. He played with the side from 1958 to 1965, helping it to win the West German league championship in 1963, to earn promotion to the Bundesliga and the 1964-65 German Cup. Konietzka also scored the historic first-ever Bundesliga goal when he tallied in the first minute against Werder Bremen on August 24, 1963.

6. When it comes to scoring a goal per-minutes played, the best Dortmund has seen so far has been forward Pierre-Emerick Aubameyang. He netted 141 goals in 213 games, scoring every 117 minutes played. Aubameyang, who was born in France but plays nationally for Gabon, suited up for Dortmund from 2013 to 2018 before leaving for Arsenal of the English Premier League. He won the Bundesliga Golden Boot in 2016-17 and helped the club win the German Cup in 2016-17 and the German Supercup in 2013 and 2014. Aubameyang was also named the Dortmund and Bundesliga Player of the Year once each and was chosen for the Bundesliga Team of the Year.

7. German international midfielder Jürgen Schütz scored 133 times in 205 contests in two different stints with his hometown team. He began his pro career with Dortmund from 1959 to 1963 and then spent several years in Italy when the Bundesliga kicked off, returning to Germany in 1968 with TSV 1860 München. Schütz was reacquired by Dortmund in 1969 and remained until 1972. Oddly, Schütz scored 159 goals in his club career but managed to notch just a combined 26 goals with the five other teams he played for.

8. The current club captain as of January 2021, Marco Reus, is still climbing the team's all-time scoring list, as he had 133 in his first 291 matches with the side. The German international midfielder joined hometown Dortmund from Borussia Mönchengladbach in 2009 and helped the squad win the German Cup in 2016-17 and the German Supercup

in 2013, 2014, and 2019. He also earned a European Champions League runner-up medal in 2012-13. Reus has been named to the Bundesliga Team of the Season six times, including five in a row, and was the league's Player of the Season three times, German Footballer of the Year twice, and the team's Player of the Year once.

9. Stéphane Chapuisat was a Swiss international striker who's credited with posting 123 goals for the club in his 284 appearances. After beginning his career in his homeland, Chapuisat joined Dortmund in 1991 and returned to play in Switzerland in 1999. He registered 102 goals in the Bundesliga in 218 outings with the club and helped it hoist the Bundesliga title in 1994-95 and 1995-96, as well as the German Supercup in 1995 and 1996, along with the European Champions League and Intercontinental Cup in 1997.

10. With 113 goals in 195 club appearances, German international striker Alfred Kelbassa ended his pro career with Dortmund between 1954 and 1963, retiring just months before the Bundesliga era kicked off. Kelbassa had begun his senior career back in 1946 after the Second World War and scored .58 goals-per-game for Dortmund, helping them earn promotion to the Bundesliga in 1962-63. It's also believed Kelbassa played the entire 90 minutes of every game during his Dortmund career and won German League titles with the side in 1956, 1957, and 1963.

CONCLUSION

Borussia Dortmund has been thrilling soccer fans for well over a century now and we've just covered the club's rich history in lighthearted trivia form for all of you fans. We hope all of your favorites have been included and we ask for forgiveness if they've been left out. However, with such a storied existence, it's virtually impossible to include everybody.

We trust you've been entertained and informed at the same time, while taking a look back at Dortmund's fascinating story, and we hope the book was perhaps also an educational learning tool for some supporters.

We assembled various challenging and informative quizzes throughout the volume's 12 chapters and also included a wide variety of "Did You Know" trivia facts. After reading the book, you should be better equipped to take on all comers in Borussia Dortmund trivia quiz challenges to prove once and for all who the top gun is.

We've made sure to include important facts regarding the club's players, trophies, and managers, as well as its transfer history, team records, and other interesting information.

Dortmund's ongoing history is certainly a magnificent one and more silverware and dramatic moments could certainly be on the horizon in the near future.

We hope reading this book will help you spread the word about your favorite team.

Made in the USA
Las Vegas, NV
02 October 2022

56411377R00075